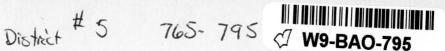

SCHOLASTIC PHONICS CLUBHOUSE™

Workbook

Aa-Dd

4 5 6 7 8 9 10   14   04 03 02 01 00 99 98

Contents

Workbook Aa–Dd

Welcome!

Aa Bb Cc Dd Ee

Ff Gg Hh Ii Jj Kk

Ll Mm Nn Oo Pp

Qq Rr Ss Tt Uu

Vv Ww Xx Yy Zz

4

Directions: Trace each child's path from left to right.

Motor Skills: Left-to-Right Progression 5

Directions: Trace each bird's path down to his or her nest. Start at the top.

Motor Skills: Top-to-Bottom Progression

Directions: Circle the two pictures on each shelf that are the same.

Directions: Color the balloon, dog, and car that is different from the others.

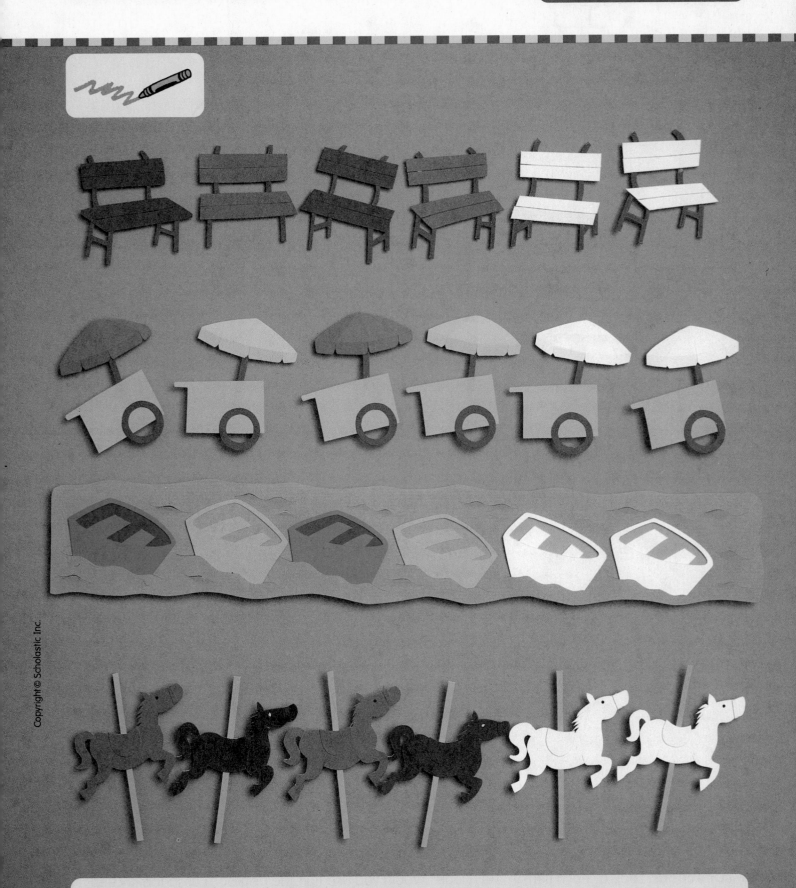

Directions: Look at the color pattern. Color the two items to continue the pattern.

Directions: Look at each item in the middle. Would you use it in the bedroom or in the kitchen? Draw a line to show where you would use it.

Frog **and** dog
rhyme.

   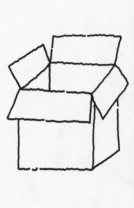

Directions: Name the two items in each picture. If the names rhyme, color the picture.

Discriminate Rhyming Sounds 11

Directions: Draw a picture of yourself. Then write your name.

Directions: Say the name of each item. Circle the item if its name begins with the **short a** sound as in **apple**.

Directions: Trace and write **A** and **a**. Say the name of each picture. Write **a** below the picture if its name begins with the **short a** sound as in **apple**.

Recognize and Write Aa

Ants in a cap.

Ants!

Ants in a can.

Ants, ants, ants!

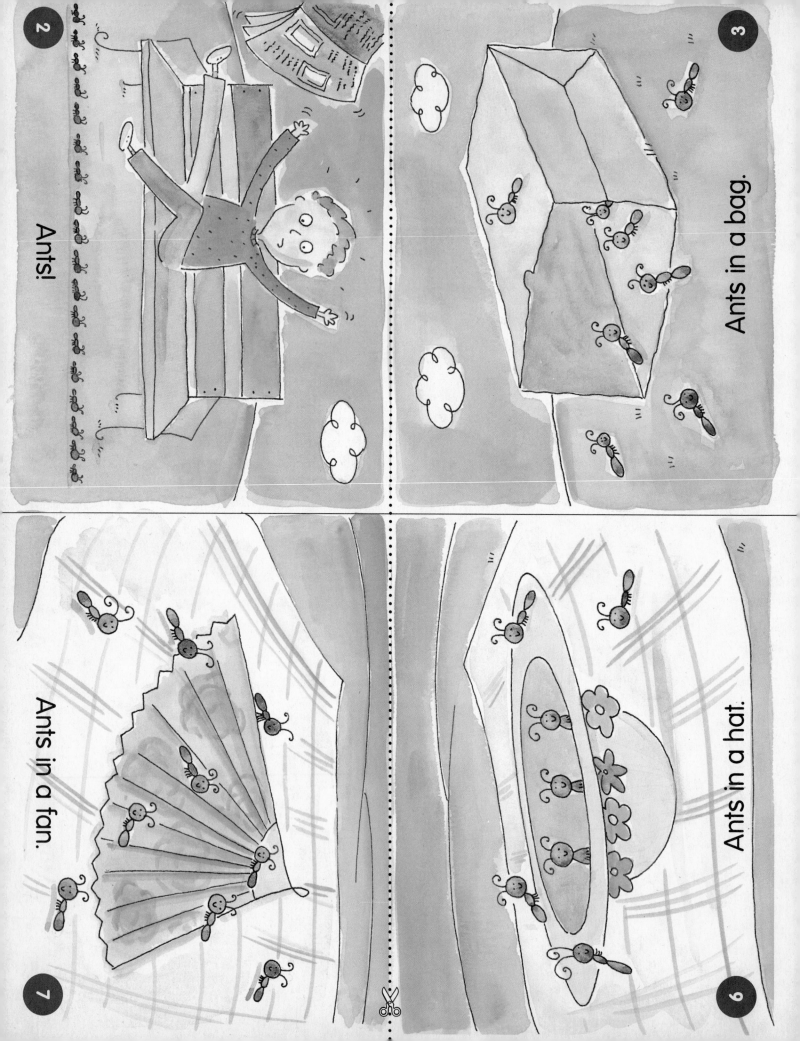

2 Ants!

3 Ants in a bag.

7 Ants in a fan.

6 Ants in a hat.

Directions: Say the name of each item. Circle the item if its name begins with the **b** sound as in **book**.

Directions: Trace and write **B** and **b**. Say the name of each picture. Color and write a **b** next to the picture if its name begins with the **b** sound as in **bus**.

18 **Recognize and Write Bb**

What can it be?

What Can It Be?

A bus.

What can it be?

What can it be?

A bear.

A bird.

What can it be?

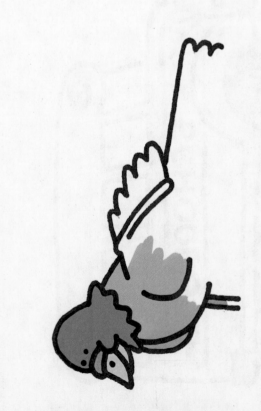

Directions: Say the name of each item. Circle the item if its name begins with the **k** sound as in **camera**.

Recognize /k/c 21

C¹

c¹

Cc

C

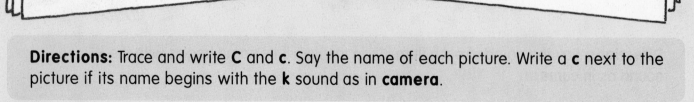

Directions: Trace and write **C** and **c**. Say the name of each picture. Write a **c** next to the picture if its name begins with the **k** sound as in **camera**.

I can see a cowboy.

I Can See ...

I can see a cow.

What can you see?

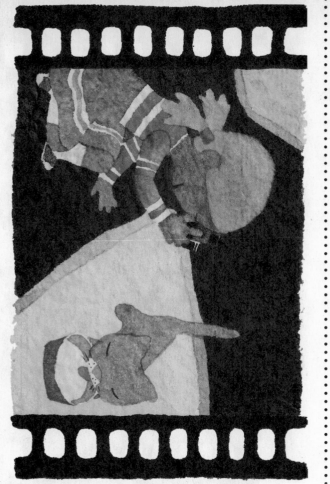

I can see a cat.

I can see a cake.

I can see a car.

I can see a camel.

Directions: Say the name of each item. Circle the item if its name begins with the **d** sound as in **desk**.

Directions: Trace and write **D** and **d**. Say the name of each picture. Color and write a **d** below the picture if its name begins with the **d** sound as in **desk**.

26 **Recognize and Write** *Dd*

We like tall dogs.

We Like Dogs

We like short dogs.

We like _____.

We like

We like big dogs.

We like little dogs.

We like happy dogs.

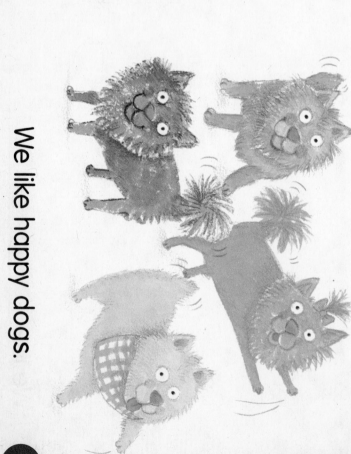

We like sad dogs.

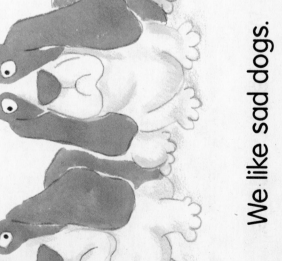

Match Capital and Small Letters: Aa, Bb, Cc, Dd

A   b

c   a

B   d

D   C

B   a

c   D

A   b

d   C

D   c

a   B

C   d

b   A

---

d   D

B   a

C   b

A   c

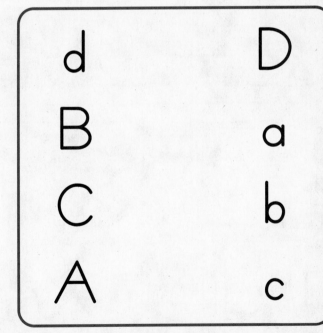

Directions: Draw lines to connect the matching capital and small letters.

Directions: Say the name of each item. Write the letter that stands for the beginning sound.

30 **Review: Aa, Bb, Cc, Dd**